This
Treasure Cove Story
belongs to

BABY SHARK AND THE TOOTH FAIRY

A CENTUM BOOK 978-1-913865-30-6
Published in Great Britain by Centum Books Ltd.
This edition published 2021.

1 3 5 7 9 10 8 6 4 2

Centum Books Ltd, 20 Devon Square, Newton Abbot,
Devon, TQ12 2HR, UK.

www.centumbooksltd.co.uk | books@centumbooksltd.co.uk
CENTUM BOOKS LIMITED. Reg. No. 07641486.

A CIP catalogue record for this book is available
from the British Library.

Printed in China.

centum

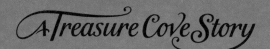

pinkfong
BABY SHARK™

Baby Shark and the Tooth Fairy

'Good morning!' says Baby Shark, beaming with a smile as bright as the sun. Wait a minute, is Baby Shark missing a tooth?

'Oh no! My tooth!'

Did Baby Shark put it somewhere to hide it from tooth thieves?

Did Baby Shark put it somewhere safe until he chomps down on his next hot clam bun?

'Oh no! I'm missing a tooth!' says Baby Shark. Yes, Baby Shark, you are!

Is his missing tooth under this big rock?
Or is it hidden in this sandcastle?
Baby Shark looks here, there and everywhere!
'Where could it be?' wonders Baby Shark.

'Is it here?

At first, Baby Shark is mad that he's lost his tooth, and then he feels afraid.

'What am I going to tell Mummy
Shark? And what if I lose another?'

That night, Baby Shark had a dream that all his teeth ran away.

'Don't leave me toothless,' he cried.

But try as he might, Baby Shark could not catch his teeth.

Without any teeth, he looked just like his grandma!

The next morning when Baby Shark woke up, he still felt sad. He had no choice but to tell his mum the news.

'Mum... Mum... I'm missing a tooth!'

'Oh, dear me! Don't worry, little one!' says Mummy Shark. 'The Tooth Fairy must have your missing tooth!' 'The Tooth Fairy?' asks Baby Shark.

'Yes, the Tooth Fairy takes the teeth you lose and brings you new ones,' says Mummy Shark.

Mummy Shark hugs Baby Shark tightly
and starts to sing a song for him.

'Baby Shark,
doo-doo-doo-doo-doo-doo.

Sharp and bright
tooth-tooth-tooth-tooth- tooth.'

That night during his dreams, Baby Shark danced with the tooth fairy all night.

As Mummy Shark
had promised,
he got a new tooth,
so sharp and bright.

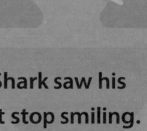

The next morning, Baby Shark saw his new tooth, and he couldn't stop smiling. 'It wasn't just a dream,' cries Baby Shark. 'The Tooth Fairy is real!'

Baby Shark swims straight to his mum.
'Mum, look at this! I've got a new
tooth!' says Baby Shark.

'What a wonderful tooth!'
says Mummy Shark.

'I won't worry so much the next time I lose a tooth!' says Baby Shark.

'See you then, Baby Shark!' says the Tooth Fairy.

The end!

Treasure Cove Stories

Please contact Centum Books to receive the full list of titles in the *Treasure Cove Stories* series.
books@centumbooksltd.co.uk

1 Three Little Pigs
2 Snow White and the Seven Dwarfs
3 The Fox and the Hound - Hide-and-Seek
4 Dumbo
5 Cinderella
6 Cinderella's Friends
7 Alice in Wonderland
8 Mad Hatter's Tea Party from Alice in Wonderland
9 Mickey Mouse and his Spaceship
10 Peter Pan
11 Pinocchio
12 Mickey and the Beanstalk
13 Sleeping Beauty and the Good Fairies
14 The Lucky Puppy
15 Chicken Little
16 The Incredibles
17 Coco
18 Winnie the Pooh and Tigger
19 The Sword in the Stone
20 Mary Poppins
21 The Jungle Book
22 Aristocats
23 Lady and the Tramp
24 Bambi
25 Bambi - Friends of the Forest
26 Pete's Dragon
27 Beauty and the Beast - The Teapot's Tale
28 Monsters, Inc. – M is for Monster
29 Finding Nemo
30 The Incredibles 2
31 The Incredibles – Jack-Jack Attack
33 Wall-E
34 Up
35 The Princess and the Frog
36 Toy Story – The Pet Problem

39 Spider-Man – Night of the Vulture!
40 Wreck it Ralph
41 Ralph Breaks the Internet
42 The Invincible Iron Man – Eye of the Dragon
45 Toy Story – A Roaring Adventure
46 Cars – Deputy Mater Saves the Day!
47 Spider-Man – Trapped by the Green Goblin
49 Spider-Man – High Voltage!
50 Frozen
51 Cinderella is my Babysitter
52 Beauty and the Beast - I am the Beast
56 I am a Princess
57 The Big Book of Paw Patrol
58 Paw Patrol - Adventures with Grandpa!
59 Paw Patrol - Pirate Pups!
60 Trolls
61 Trolls Holiday
63 Zootropolis
64 Ariel is my Babysitter
65 Tiana is my Babysitter
66 Belle is my Babysitter
67 Paw Patrol - Itty-Bitty Kitty Rescue
68 Moana
70 Guardians of the Galaxy
71 Captain America - High-Stakes Heist!
72 Ant-Man
73 The Mighty Avengers
74 The Mighty Avengers - Lights Out!
75 The Incredible Hulk
78 Paw Patrol - All-Star Pups!
80 I am Ariel
82 Jasmine is my Babysitter
87 Beauty and the Beast - I am Belle
88 The Lion Guard - The Imaginary Okapi
89 Thor - Thunder Strike!
90 Guardians of the Galaxy - Rocket to the Rescue!
93 Olaf's Frozen Adventure
95 Trolls - Branch's Bunker Birthday

96 Trolls - Poppy's Party
97 The Ugly Duckling
98 Cars - Look Out for Mater!
99 101 Dalmatians
100 The Sorcerer's Apprentice
101 Tangled
102 Avengers – The Threat of Thanos
105 The Mighty Thor
106 Doctor Strange
107 Captain Marvel
108 The Invincible Iron Man
110 The Big Freeze
111 Ratatouille
112 Aladdin
113 Aladdin - I am the Genie
114 Seven Dwarfs Find a House
115 Toy Story
116 Toy Story 4
117 Paw Patrol - Jurassic Bark!
118 Paw Patrol - Mighty Pup Power!
121 The Lion King - I am Simba
122 Winnie the Pooh - The Honey Tree
123 Frozen II
124 Baby Shark and the Colours of the Ocean
125 Baby Shark and the Police Sharks!
126 Trolls World Tour
127 I am Elsa
128 I am Anna
129 I am Olaf
130 I am Mulan
131 Sleeping Beauty
132 Onward
133 Paw Patrol – Puppy Birthday to You!
134 Black Widow
135 Trolls – Poppy's Big Day!
136 Baby Shark and the Tooth Fairy
137 Baby Shark – Mummy Shark
138 Inside Out
139 The Prince and the Pauper
140 Finding Dory
142 The Lion King - Simba's Daring Rescue

Book list may be subject to change. Not all titles are listed.